# God Bless America

# God Bless America

Words and music by *Irving Berlin*
Illustrations by *Lynn Munsinger*

SCHOLASTIC INC.
New York   Toronto   London   Auckland   Sydney
Mexico City   New Delhi   Hong Kong   Buenos Aires

God bless America,

Land that I love,

Stand beside her

And guide her

Through the night with a light from above.

From the mountains,

To the prairies,

To the oceans white with foam,

God bless America,

My home sweet home.

# God Bless America

Words and Music by
IRVING BERLIN

While the storm clouds gather * Far across the sea,

Let us swear allegiance * To a land that's free;

Let us all be grateful * For a land so fair,

As we raise our voices * In a solemn prayer.

"God Bless America" by Irving Berlin was first published in 1938. Almost as soon as the song began generating revenue, Mr. Berlin established the God Bless America Fund to benefit American youth. Most of the earnings from "God Bless America" have been donated to two youth organizations with which Mr. and Mrs. Berlin were personally involved: the Girl Scout Council of Greater New York, and the Greater New York Councils of the Boy Scouts of America. These councils do not discriminate on any basis and are committed to serving all segments of New York City's diverse youth population.

The trustees of the God Bless America Fund are working with the two councils to ensure that funding is allocated for New York City children affected by the tragic events of September 11, 2001.

*A portion of the publisher's proceeds is also being donated to the God Bless America Fund.*

To the children of New York and
their friends everywhere
—*L.M.*

ISBN 0-439-56213-9

12 11 10 9 8 7 6 5 4 3 2          3 4 5 6 7 8/0

Printed in the U.S.A.          40

First Scholastic printing, September 2003